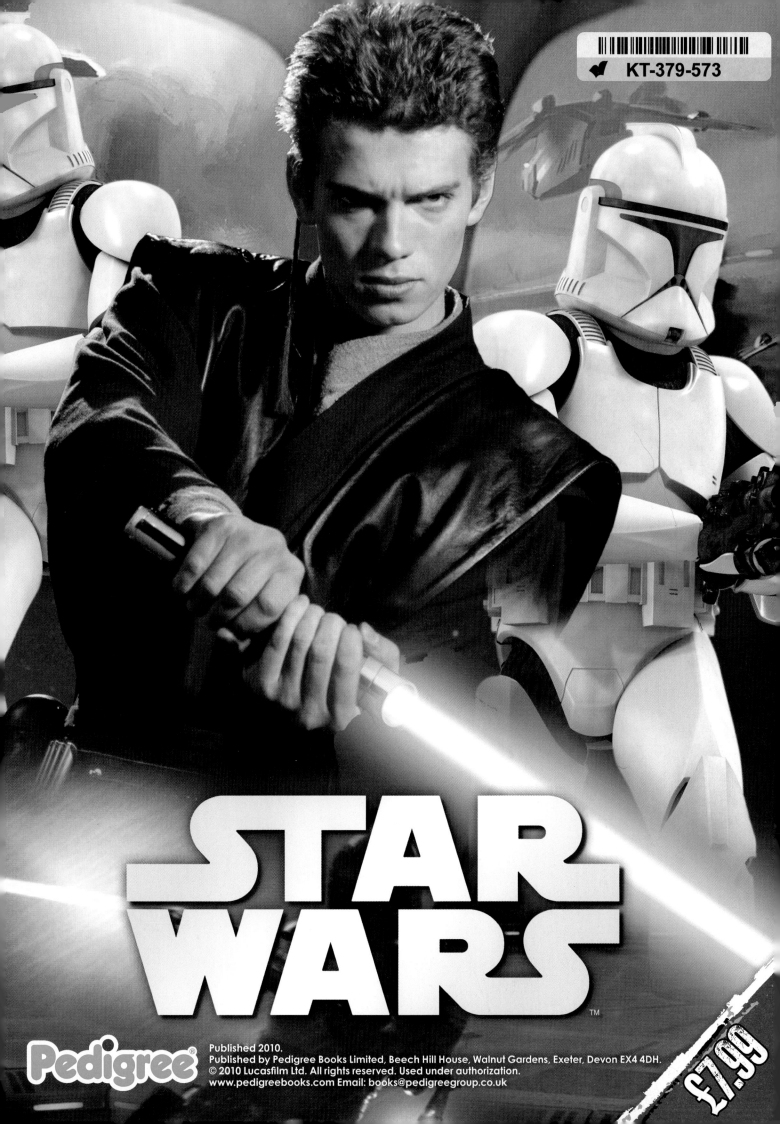

STAR WARS™

£7.99

Pedigree®

Published 2010.
Published by Pedigree Books Limited, Beech Hill House, Walnut Gardens, Exeter, Devon EX4 4DH.
© 2010 Lucasfilm Ltd. All rights reserved. Used under authorization.
www.pedigreebooks.com Email: books@pedigreegroup.co.uk

WELCOME FELLOW TRAVELLER!

You are at the beginning of one of the greatest adventures of all time. My loyal friends and faithful companions worked tirelessly to defeat the Emperor and restore the Republic. We in the Rebel Alliance are determined to succeed!

To understand the events that led to this moment, it is necessary to go far back in time… back to the day when a Jedi Master met a small slave boy, and the future of the galaxy was altered forever.

JOIN US ON THE MOST EXCITING ADVENTURE OF OUR LIVES – AND MAY THE FORCE BE WITH YOU!

Contents

REBEL PROFILE

Do you wish to join the ranks of those who are loyal to the Jedi and the Republic? Complete these sections to tell us more about you.

NAME: Sh@un gemmell

BIRTHDAY: 21.07.00

HOME PLANET: Earth

SPECIES: humam

TRANSPORT:

FAITHFUL COMPANION:

GREATEST STRENGTH:

GREATEST WEAKNESS:

AMBITION:

ALLEGIANCE: unsc

HERO: MC

GALACTIC QUIZ PART 1

ANSWER THESE QUESTIONS TO DISCOVER HOW MUCH YOU REALLY KNOW ABOUT THE START OF OUR ADVENTURE!

1 IN WHAT YEAR DID THE TRADE FEDERATION BLOCKADE THE PLANET OF NABOO?

2 WHO WAS THE SUPREME CHANCELLOR AT THAT TIME?

3 WHICH DROID HELPED THE JEDI ESCAPE FROM NABOO WITH QUEEN AMIDALA?

4 WHO WAS THE JUNK DEALER QUI-GON JINN MET ON TATOOINE?

5 WHO WAS ANAKIN'S MAIN RIVAL IN THE PODRACE?

6 WHICH GUNGAN LEADER ALLIED WITH QUEEN AMIDALA?

7 WHERE DID ANAKIN HIDE AT THE START OF THE BATTLE WITH THE TRADE FEDERATION?

8 WHO DESTROYED THE MAIN REACTOR OF THE DROID CONTROL SHIP?

9 WHO WAS THE SITH APPRENTICE?

10 WHICH NABOO CITIZEN WAS ELECTED SUPREME CHANCELLOR?

SCORE:

Pick Out Palpatine

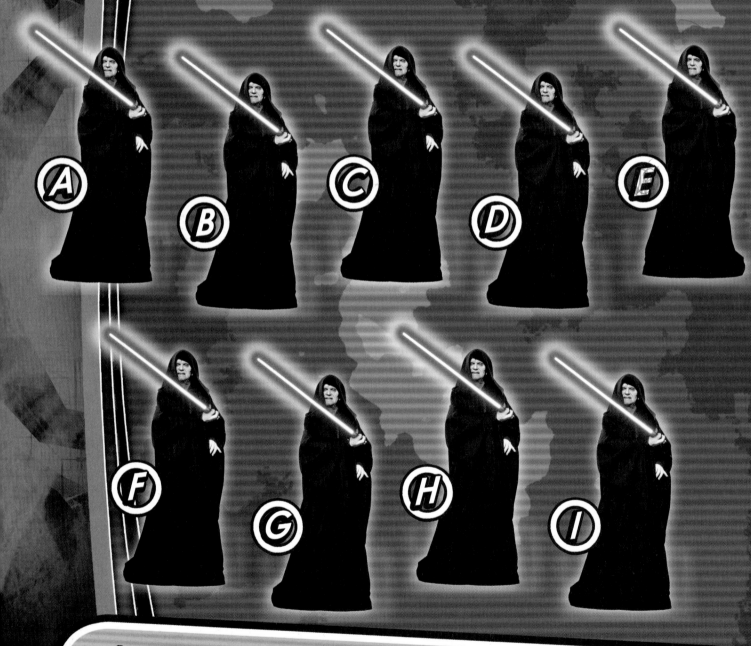

(A)
(B)
(C)
(D)
(E)
(F)
(G)
(H)
(I)

Look closely at these pictures of Palpatine. One of them doesn't match the others. Can you spot the odd one out?

GUNGAN GRID

Use the grid to copy this picture of Boss Nass and then complete the portrait by colouring him in.

Ingress/Egress Hatch

Main Trans Viewport

Front Vi

Knee Joints

THE GALACTIC REPUBLIC

The Galactic Republic was based on good values and principles, but it had become corrupt. It was too bogged down by red tape and regulations to be able to achieve any real change. There were also some Senators who were only interested in their own goals. Senators like Padmé Amidala worked hard to change the system from within. But Count Dooku's Separatist movement was steadily destroying the democratic system. The Clone Wars raged across the galaxy, but no one could have guessed that the real threat to democracy and freedom sat within the walls of the Senate itself.

GALACTIC SENATE

Each member world of the Republic chose a Senator to represent them. These Senators were ambassadors of their home planet. The Senators elected a Supreme Chancellor for a set length of time.

Member worlds kept their own governments, although they had to obey laws passed by the Senate. The Senate was based on the planet Coruscant.

SUPREME CHANCELLOR PALPATINE

Palpatine appeared to be the saviour of the Republic. He took over from a weak Chancellor and brought strength and decisiveness to the Republic. However, he was secretly carrying out a dark and evil plan. He had spent years studying the Sith Order and was now a fully-fledged Sith Master.

One of Palpatine's greatest qualities was patience. He was prepared to wait for as long as necessary until he could seize absolute power.

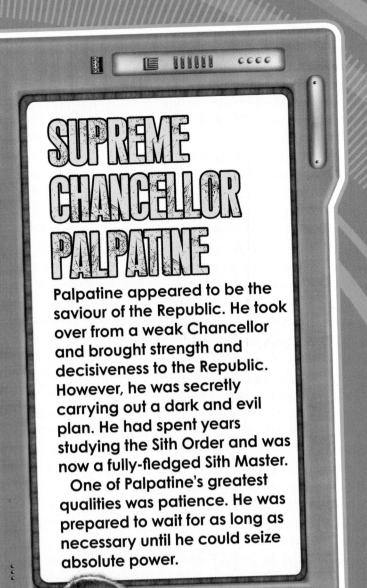

SENATOR PADMÉ AMIDALA

Padmé was a passionate idealist who had worked in politics since her teenage years. She had served as Queen of Naboo, but it was as Senator that she really found her true calling.

Padmé worked tirelessly to achieve peace and stability in the galaxy. When she saw Palpatine seizing absolute power, she knew that democracy and liberty had died. This, and the treachery of her husband Anakin, broke her heart and resulted in her death.

THE ARMY OF THE REPUBLIC

The Republic did not have a military force when the Trade Federation blockaded Naboo. They relied on the peace-keeping Jedi Knights. However, the Clone Wars changed everything. A fighting force was needed, and it took the form of a clone army. Unbeknown to the Jedi, they had been created in secret as part of the Sith's wicked plan to destroy the Republic.

THE BATTLE OF GEONOSIS

This key moment in the fate of the Republic came about following the capture of Obi-Wan Kenobi, Anakin Skywalker and Padmé Amidala. The Separatists were preparing to watch their prisoners torn apart by beasts in an arena. The Jedi arrived with clone troopers in time to save the prisoners, but this event was the start of the Clone Wars that would destroy them and the Republic.

THE JEDI COUNCIL

The Jedi Order defended the Galactic Republic. The most senior Jedi served on the Jedi Council, and they had a certain amount of political power. However, when Palpatine became Supreme Chancellor, he began to put pressure on the Council to follow his orders.

THE CLONE WARS

When several member worlds united to separate from the Republic, events escalated to the point of war. The Senate voted to give Palpatine emergency powers, and Palpatine approved the use of the vast clone army. The next stage of the Sith plan had begun.

ORDER 66

The end of the Republic came about after the death of General Grievous. When the Jedi realised who the Sith Master was, Palpatine revealed his true colours. His hold over Anakin Skywalker made it possible for him to turn the Jedi to the dark side. He issued Order 66, and clone troopers across the galaxy turned on their Jedi generals. In the space of a few hours, the Jedi were almost completely destroyed.

SENATOR BAIL ORGANA

Bail Organa was a trusted advisor in Palpatine's Republic, but he grew increasingly worried by the direction in which the Chancellor was taking the galaxy. With Padmé Amidala, he began to question the war effort.

His concerns crystallised into opposition after Order 66 destroyed the Jedi. His kind and fair nature was appalled by Palpatine's actions, and he became a friend of the Rebel Alliance. After Padmé died, Bail Organa adopted one of her twins, Leia. Thanks to him, Leia thrived and followed her mother's path into politics.

ENEMY IN HIDING

SOLVE THESE CLUES TO COMPLETE THE CROSSWORD. THE LETTERS IN THE SHADED SQUARES CAN BE REARRANGED INTO THE NAME OF A DEADLY ENEMY OF THE JEDI.

1.

2.

3.

4.

5.

6.

7.

8.

1 The Order that Darth Sidious followed

2 A repulsive and grotesque Tatooine dweller

3 The Emperor's home world

4 A Jedi apprentice

5 A Wookiee who was rescued from a slave ship

6 Padmé's relationship to Anakin

7 Where was the Galactic Senate based?

8 A wise and aged Jedi Master

THE ENEMY IN HIDING IS:

SHADOW SPOTTER

CAN YOU PUT NAMES TO EACH OF THESE SHADOWS? LOOK CAREFULLY AT EACH ONE AND THEN FILL IN THE CORRECT NAME.

17

THE PHANTOM MENACE

1 The Trade Federation has placed a blockade of starships around Naboo.

3 Darth Sidious orders Nute Gunray to kill the Jedi.

2 Supreme Chancellor Valorum sends two Jedi Knights to settle the conflict.

4 Obi-Wan and Qui-Gon must warn Queen Amidala of the danger.

6 The Jedi travel underwater to the Naboo capital city.

5 Obi-Wan and Qui-Gon meet Jar Jar Binks.

7 The Jedi rescue the Queen and her handmaidens.

8 They escape and head for Coruscant to ask the Senate for help.

9 Darth Sidious orders his apprentice Darth Maul to find the Queen.

10 The Jedi have to stop on Tatooine to refuel and repair the ship.

11 A dealer called Watto has the parts they need, but Qui-Gon has no money.

12 Slave boy Anakin Skywalker enters a podrace to win the money for Qui-Gon.

THE PHANTOM MENACE

13 The Force is strong with Anakin. Qui-Gon hopes to train the boy as a Jedi.

15 While the race is on, Darth Maul is seeking the Jedi.

14 Darth Maul sends probe droids to find the Queen.

16 Sebulba crashes as Anakin speeds to victory!

18 Qui-Gon and Darth Maul have a fierce duel, but Qui-Gon escapes.

17 Anakin goes with the Jedi, but is sad to leave his mother.

19 On Coruscant, Senator Palpatine suggests a vote of no confidence in the Chancellor

20 The Queen decides to return to Naboo with the Jedi

21 Qui-Gon tells the Jedi Council about Anakin

22 The Council sense fear in Anakin and refuse to train him.

23 Lord Sidious sends Darth Maul to Naboo.

24 On Naboo, Padmé reveals that she is Queen Amidala!

THE PHANTOM MENACE

25 Padmé and Boss Nass become allies and draw up a plan

26 Padmé and her team creep into the city and hurry into the landing area.

27 Droideka droids open fire and Darth Maul attacks the Jedi.

28 Anakin shoots down the droidekas and flies up into space on autopilot.

30 The Gungans are battling bravely.

29 Padmé and her team capture the Viceroy.

31 Anakin destroys the Droid Control Ship.

32 Darth Maul plunges his lightsaber into Qui-Gon's stomach.

33 Obi-Wan slashes Darth Maul in half.

34 Before Qui-Gon dies, he asks Obi-Wan to train Anakin as a Jedi.

35 Palpatine is elected Supreme Chancellor.

36 The blockade is over, but dark times lie ahead.

Words of Power

In ancient times, it was believed that knowing a person's name gave you power over them. Some words have the ability to delight, terrify and amaze. Can you find all these powerful words in the grid?

```
P J I J T K S S P D F R C K U D
E F O R C E G L I N G E D U G C
G E Q W U O V F M E E G J F H W
O A R F W L Y O J D I N O T A G
L R N G R G H O L O Y A L T Y X
M U B J Q G P R O E A F H I T H
A K S S U D H C S T R W S D U T
D N F P R O M I S E A C T W W F
M P H F P H A D I N B R E D R E
I L T E I R U G F E G A R U O C
P M E X L J Y P L T K O P H F N
O J D P L K S I R E N I D Y F A
M U S E P P E A S I H E L N F T
J O H R T V N C Q L A G H Y S S
K T D I E T U E F T E O D L T I
O R J E W W L T H T G N E R T S
T J K N E L L D G E V I H J O E
F D S C C R G P W F E K D U G R
N T H E O K F Q C E T D J L A Z
```

- FORCE
- STRENGTH
- LOVE
- DEATH
- FEAR
- RESISTANCE
- LOSS
- COURAGE
- BELIEF
- PROMISE
- LOYALTY
- FREEDOM
- HOPE
- ANGER
- EXPERIENCE

BUILD YOUR OWN DROID

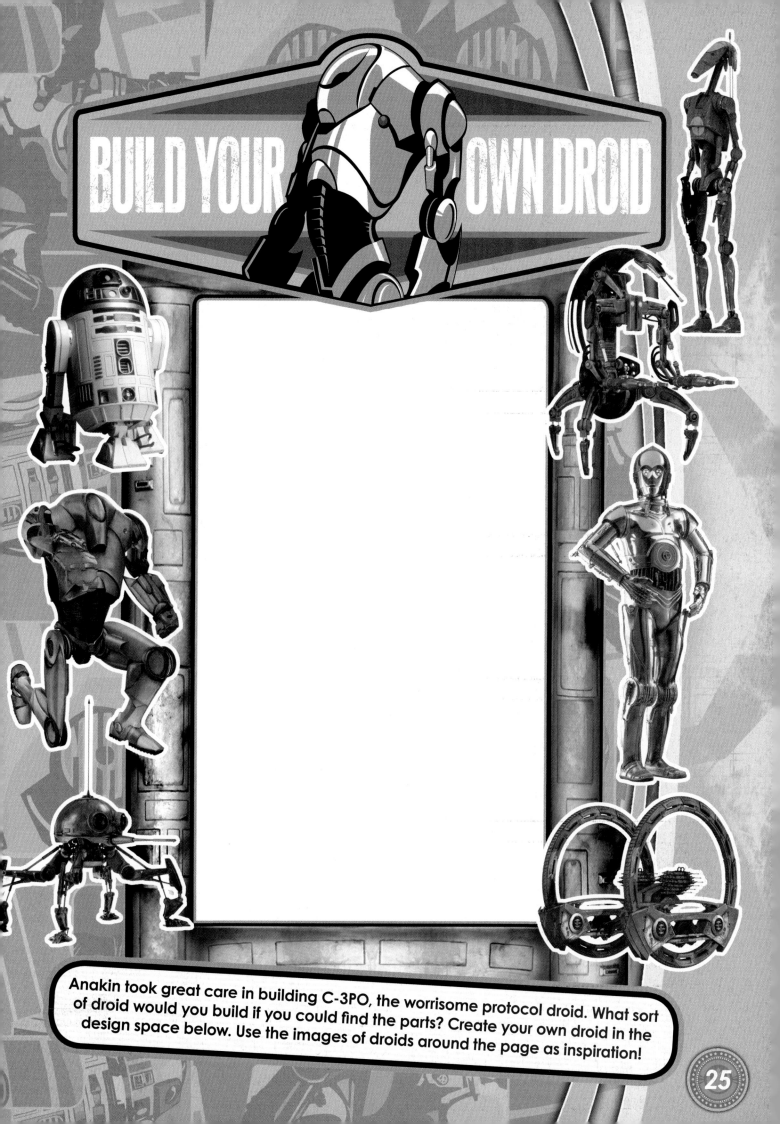

Anakin took great care in building C-3PO, the worrisome protocol droid. What sort of droid would you build if you could find the parts? Create your own droid in the design space below. Use the images of droids around the page as inspiration!

HOW TO DRAW JAR JAR BINKS

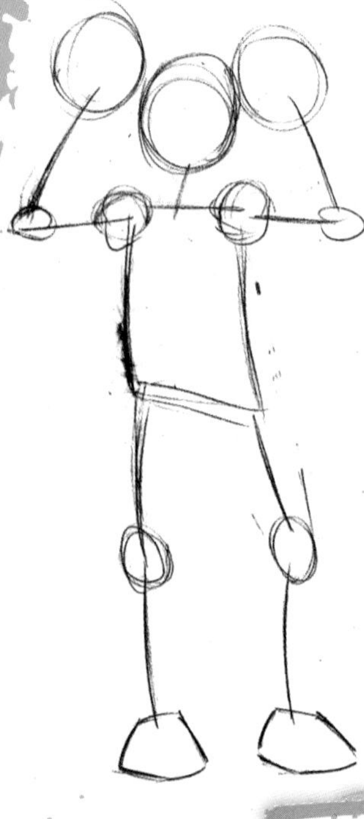

Draw pencil lines to mark out the position of Jar Jar's body, arms and legs. Use circles to show his head, hands, feet and joints.

STEP 1

Jar Jar Binks was a loyal friend to Padmé Amidala and Anakin Skywalker. Follow these steps to create your own picture of this accident-prone Gungan.

Draw a rough outline of Jar Jar's body shape. Roughly sketch in his big eyes and tongue.

STEP 2

Start to add the detail of his clothing, toes and fingers.

STEP 3

Add shading and smaller details, rubbing out the rough pencil lines as you go.

Finalise your drawing with a fine ink pen.

STEP 5

The Gungans and the Naboo

The beautiful planet of Naboo is inhabited by the Naboo and the Gungans. Its landscape is made up of swamps, plains and green hills.

Unlike many other planets, Naboo does not have a molten core. Inside the planet is a massive honeycomb structure, creating hundreds of caves and tunnels. The core is inhabited by several strange and dangerous creatures.

The long-standing rift between the Naboo and the Gungans was non-violent. They didn't understand each other, but they never fought a war with each other. However, it took an invasion of their planet to truly bring them together.

Theed

Naboo's capital city is known for its grand libraries, museums and theatres. It is seen as one of the Naboo's greatest achievements. The city is large, but it fits perfectly within its environment, because the Naboo have a strong belief in ecological conservation.

Otoh Gunga

The largest Gungan city on Naboo is hidden deep in Lake Paonga. It is a collection of beautiful bubble buildings, which do not allow water to get inside. The bubbles are anchored to mighty stone pillars on the lake's bed.

The floors of Otoh Gunga look as if they are to be covered in precious stones, and fine Gungan artwork is displayed all over the city.

Queen Amidala

Padmé Naberrie was trained from an early age to enter the world of leadership and politics. She became Theed's supervisor at the age of twelve, and took on the title 'Amidala' as her name of state.

Padmé was just fourteen years old when she became Queen, and within a few months she was facing a unique crisis – the Trade Federation blockade. She was very well trained and a gifted diplomat, and she led her people through this difficult time with courage and dignity.

Like all Naboo rulers, when she was Queen, Padmé wore dramatic makeup and elaborate clothes. This was designed to disguise her true appearance, as well as giving her an air of mystery and majesty.

As a ruler she was kind, fair and wise – all that could be hoped for. To the people of Naboo she came to represent the spirit of her nation.

Jar Jar Binks

Jar Jar Binks was orphaned when his parents' home bubble was destroyed by a sea monster. Since then, he never seemed to fit in anywhere – until he met a couple of Jedi knights on the surface of Naboo.

When he met Obi-Wan and Qui-Gon, Jar Jar had been banished from Otoh Gunga because he was clumsy. He helped them to reach Theed and became a freedom fighter, ultimately helping to bring the Naboo and the Gungans together in harmony.

Following the Battle of Naboo, Jar Jar was selected as the Gungan ambassador to Theed. He went on to serve as Senior Representative of Naboo in the Galactic Senate. For the first time, he really seemed to belong somewhere.

Boss Nass

Boss Nass was the leader of the Gungans when the Trade Federation invaded the planet. He had a quick temper, but he admired courage and humility and he saw both these qualities in Queen Amidala of the Naboo. Boss Nass made an alliance between the Gungans and the Naboo, which led to the Trade Federation's defeat.

When the galaxy fell under the Emperor's control, Boss Nass became a Rebel sympathiser. He worked with the Rebel Alliance to cause the Emperor as much trouble as possible.

The Battle of Naboo

The Battle of Naboo began because the Trade Federation invaded the planet to protest against the taxation of trade routes. The invasion overwhelmed the Naboo. Battle tanks entered the city of Theed from all directions.

Queen Amidala escaped and asked the Galactic Senate for help, but the Senate was too bogged down in formalities to be able to take decisive action.

Queen Amidala returned to Naboo and made peace with Boss Nass, ruler of the Gungans. They united against the invaders and worked together to drive them out of Naboo.

The Gungan army drew the Trade Federation army away from Theed, allowing Amidala's forces to enter the city. Fighter pilots flew starfighters against the Trade Federation's droid control ship, and thanks to Anakin Skywalker, the droid control ship was destroyed.

Many lives were lost during the Battle of Naboo, and its consequences were far-reaching. The Trade Federation was defeated, and the Gungans and Naboo formed a lasting peace. However, the invasion showed other member planets that they could not rely on the Republic to protect them.

The Queen's Handmaidens

This group of young women was handpicked to aid the Queen. They helped her with her dresses, her hair and her makeup. However, they were far more than beauty assistants.

Each handmaiden was trained in self-defence and could protect the Queen in many ways. Sometimes, that might involve posing as her, so each of them had to bear a resemblance to the Queen.

All of the handmaidens had special skills, and were immensely brave. They were prepared to lose their lives to defend their sovereign. Handmaidens usually wore crimson cloaks, trousers, tunics, boots and overcoats, sometimes with blasters strapped to their waists.

CODE BREAKER

A MESSAGE HAS BEEN INTERCEPTED BY THE JEDI AND MAY CONTAIN A CLUE TO HELP IDENTIFY THE SITH MASTER. THE JEDI HAVE STARTED DECODING IT, BUT NOW THEY'RE STUCK. CAN YOU FINISH CRACKING THE TOUGH CODE AND READ THE MESSAGE?

%>! 3@%> 5+! 8~@3!6 %~ +!%"+4 %~ 8~=!+.

3~~4 %>! 2!6@ =@££ *! 4~ 1~+!.

%>! 65+< 3@6! ~/ %>! /~+?! @3 1~+! 8~=!+/"£. @% ?544~% *! 6!/!5%!6.

=! 6~ 4~% =54% *5£54?!. =! =54% %>! 2!6@ %~ *! 6!3%+~±!6.

1± +~£! =@%>@4 %>! 3!45%! 8+~%!?%%3 1! /+~1 5££ 3"38@?@~4.

%>!± =@££ 4!9!+ @6!4%@/± 1! "4%@£ @% @3 %~~ £5%!.

A	B	C	D	E	F	G	H	I	J	K	L	M
*		6	!		7			2	<			

N	O	P	Q	R	S	T	U	V	W	X	Y	Z
4	8	$		3		"	9			±	^	

32

ALIEN CREATOR

The Jedi encounter all sorts of beings on their travels, from insect-like Geonosians to small, friendly Ewoks. If you had the power to design an alien being, what would it look like? Use this space to form your own creation.

GALACTIC QUIZ PART 2

CAN YOU ANSWER ALL THESE QUESTIONS CORRECTLY? CHECK YOUR ANSWERS AND FILL IN YOUR SCORE.

1 HOW MANY YEARS PASSED BEFORE ANAKIN AND PADMÉ MET AGAIN ON CORUSCANT?

2 WHO OWNED R2-D2 WHEN THE JEDI WERE ASSIGNED TO PROTECT SENATOR AMIDALA?

3 WHO HELPED OBI-WAN TO IDENTIFY THE KAMINO TOXIC DART?

4 WHAT WAS DIFFERENT ABOUT THE CLONE THAT JANGO WAS RAISING AS HIS SON?

5 WHY DID ANAKIN GO BACK TO TATOOINE?

6 DID ANAKIN TELL PADMÉ WHAT HE DID TO THE TUSKEN RAIDERS?

7 WHERE DID JANGO FETT AND HIS SON FLY TO FROM KAMINO?

8 WHO WAS COUNT DOOKU'S MASTER?

9 WHICH ARM DID ANAKIN LOSE?

10 WHO WAS GRANTED EMERGENCY POWERS BY THE SENATE?

SCORE:

ATTACK OF THE CLONES

1 Count Dooku has persuaded many solar systems to leave the Republic.

2 Some Senators want an army, but the Jedi prefer peaceful negotiations.

3 Someone is trying to kill Senator Amidala. Obi-Wan and Anakin must protect her.

4 Anakin has loved Padmé for ten years, but she still thinks of him as a child.

5 Obi-Wan and Anakin foil a midnight attack on Padmé's life.

6 They chase the assassin through the busy skies of Coruscant.

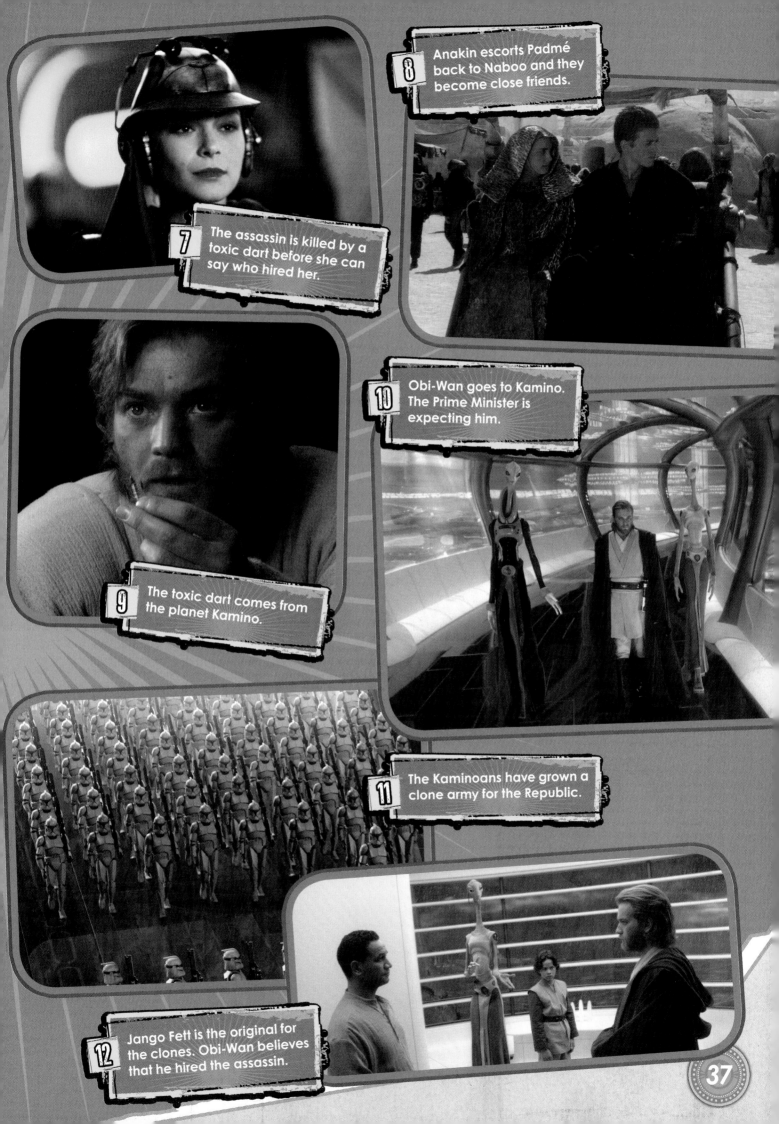

8 Anakin escorts Padmé back to Naboo and they become close friends.

7 The assassin is killed by a toxic dart before she can say who hired her.

10 Obi-Wan goes to Kamino. The Prime Minister is expecting him.

9 The toxic dart comes from the planet Kamino.

11 The Kaminoans have grown a clone army for the Republic.

12 Jango Fett is the original for the clones. Obi-Wan believes that he hired the assassin.

13 Padmé and Anakin fall deeply in love, but Jedi are not allowed to marry.

14 Anakin dreams that his mother is in danger. He and Padmé fly to Tatooine to find her.

15 Obi-Wan follows Jango Fett to Geonosis.

16 Obi-Wan finds the Separatists on Geonosis with a huge army of battle droids.

17 Obi-Wan sends a message to Anakin, but then he is captured.

18 Anakin's mother has been kidnapped by Tusken Raiders.

19 Anakin finds the Tusken Raiders' camp, but his mother dies in his arms.

20 Anakin slaughters the Tusken Raiders with his lightsaber.

21 Anakin and Padmé set off to rescue Obi-Wan.

22 The Senate grants Palpatine emergency powers.

23 Padmé and Anakin are captured on Geonosis and condemned to death.

24 They are tied up in the execution arena with Obi-Wan.

39

ATTACK OF THE CLONES

25 Padmé, Obi-Wan and Anakin overpower the wild beasts.

26 A cloaked figure holds a lightsaber to Jango Fett's throat. It's Mace Windu.

27 All around the arena, Jedi they pull off their cloaks and ignite their lightsabers.

28 Dooku summons his droids into the arena and an epic battle begins.

29 Jango Fett joins the battle, and Mace Windu cuts off his head.

30 A fleet of clone gunships swoops out of the sky, led by Yoda.

31 The droid army retreats, and Count Dooku flees.

32 Anakin and Obi-Wan battle Count Dooku, but are defeated.

33 But Dooku cannot defeat Yoda. He creates a distraction and escapes.

34 Anakin and Padmé get married in secret.

35 On Coruscant, thousands of clone troopers march into battle ships.

36 Palpatine is pleased, but Yoda feels sad and worried.

USE THE FORCE!

START — 01 — 02 — 03 — You are put in charge of a squadron. Advance three spaces

05

10 — 09 — Darth Vader fires on you – take evasive manoeuvres and miss a turn — 07 — 06

11

WHO WILL BE FIRST TO FIRE ON THE DEATH STAR'S THERMAL EXHAUST PORT AND DESTROY THE EMPEROR'S CREATION? USE THE FORCE TO BRING YOU GOOD LUCK WITH THE DICE – THE FIRST TO REACH THE THERMAL EXHAUST PORT IS THE WINNER!

You destroy a droid starfighter! Have another turn — 13 — 14 — 20

19

You will need a counter for each player and a dice. Work your way around the board and try to avoid your enemies and the dangers of battle. The winner is the first player to reach the thermal exhaust port, but be careful – you have to throw exactly the right number to reach the port and destroy the Death Star!

Your friend's starfighter is destroyed. Retreat three spaces

16 — 17 — An enemy starfighter crashes into the Death Star. Advance two spaces

34 - **35** -

You hear the voice of Obi-Wan Kenobi! Have another turn

- **37** - **38**

33

39

32 - **31** -

You are outnumbered by enemy starfighters. Retreat two spaces

You fire on the target but fail to hit the port! Return to square 1

29

41

You are finding it hard to feel the Force. Retreat four spaces

28

42

23

27

43

24 - **25** -

Your best friend comes to your rescue! Advance three spaces

FINISH

43

THE JEDI AND THE SITH

Like two sides of the same coin, the Jedi and the Sith are eternally connected and eternally opposing. While the Jedi believe in using the Force for the good of the many, the Sith believe in using it for the good of oneself. While the Jedi turn away from the dark side of the Force, the Sith encourage it.

THE JEDI ORDER

The ancient Jedi Order was a group of protectors who shared a common belief in the Force. Jedi trained, studied and developed within the Jedi Temple on Coruscant. They were governed by the Jedi Council, which was made up of twelve senior and respected Jedi. They communicated between the Jedi and the Republic government.

YODA

Yoda was one of the most experienced and respected Jedi Masters. He sat on the Jedi Council, and his age and wisdom made him an inspiring and insightful teacher. He was also a Form IV lightsaber combat master, which emphasised acrobatics, but he preferred careful thought to rash action.

MACE WINDU

Mace Windu was a gifted warrior and a wise diplomat. His sense of humour and whimsical side were a great asset to him, and he was very strong in the Force. Although he preferred to seek peaceful solutions, he had a complete mastery over Jedi fighting styles.

ANAKIN SKYWALKER

Anakin Skywalker was born a slave, but he was destined to be one of the most legendary figures of all time. Bold, reckless, impatient and loving, he became one of the shining stars of the Jedi Academy, and the source of endless trouble for his Master, Obi-Wan Kenobi.

He had no father – some thought he had been created by the will of the Force itself. As the Chosen One, he was expected to one day bring balance to the Force. But not even the Jedi could guess how this would be achieved.

THE FORCE

The Force is an energy field that connects and is part of all living things. A Jedi uses this connection to the living Force to overcome the limitations of the physical form, and to attain deep wisdom. Younglings are trained to use the Force to see, rather than using their physical senses.

OBI-WAN KENOBI

Kind, gentle and wise, Obi-Wan Kenobi was a staunch friend and a talented Jedi. He was resourceful and quick-thinking, and he always put the needs of others before himself. His inner focus was powerful and steady, and he had a masterful connection to the Force.

THE JEDI CODE

There is no emotion;
there is peace.

There is no ignorance;
there is knowledge.

There is no passion;
there is serenity.

There is no death;
there is the Force.

THE LOST TWENTY

Only twenty Jedi have ever deliberately left the Order. They are known as the Lost Twenty. A failed Jedi can be a very serious threat, because the dark side of the Force is most tempting to those with the least patience.

45

THE SITH ORDER

DARTH SIDIOUS

THE SITH ORDER

The Sith Order devoted its energy and desire to the dark side of the Force. They cared only about personal gain and were prepared to do anything to achieve their goals.

The secret identity of the seemingly kindly Supreme Chancellor was ambitious, greedy and cruel. He rose to power through cunning, deception and treachery. His ability to anticipate how others would react enabled him to plot the downfall of the Republic.

DARTH MAUL

This dark warrior's past is shrouded in mystery. It is known that he was passionately devoted to the Sith cause, and his body was covered in Sith tattoos. Maul used a double-bladed lightsaber and was driven by a hatred of the Jedi Order. He was killed by Obi-Wan Kenobi during the Battle of Naboo.

DARTH TYRANUS

Count Dooku had once been a Jedi Master, but his greed and impatience turned him to the dark side of the Force. He became apprentice to Darth Sidious, who encouraged him to start a Separatist movement. He was a skilled warrior and a man of deadly cunning.

DARTH VADER

When Anakin Skywalker turned to the dark side, he became Darth Vader. As a Sith, he was unforgiving and vengeful. He locked away all trace of the man he had been, and his imposing armour made him seem more machine than human. He struck terror into the hearts of his enemies.

ANCIENT HISTORY

Long ago, some of the Jedi wanted to access the power of the Force's dark side. Because this went against the Jedi Code, they were exiled from the Republic.

These Dark Jedi travelled through the galaxy and settled on a planet called Korriban, where they found a race called the Sith who were strong in the Force. After thousands of years, and the word 'Sith' came to describe the Dark Jedi as well as the people of Korriban.

There were many terrible conflicts between the Jedi of the Republic and the Sith. After a decisive last battle on the plains of Ruusan, the Jedi were victorious. However, one Sith escaped: Darth Bane.

Darth Bane rebuilt the Sith Order in secret, structuring a cult that could flourish in the shadows. Cunning, subterfuge and stealth lay at the heart of the Sith order.

Bane decreed that there should only ever be two Sith at any time – a master and an apprentice. Traditionally, the apprentice would eventually kill the master and take on an apprentice of his own.

SENSING THE DARK SIDE

The dark side is often very hard to detect, even by those who are strong in the Force. Darth Sidious was able to keep his true self a secret for many years, even though he worked closely with the Jedi.

GALACTIC QUIZ PART 3

1 WHICH GENERAL HAD A BAG THAT CONTAINED HIS INNARDS?

2 WHOSE HEAD AND HANDS DID ANAKIN CUT OFF?

3 WHAT WONDERFUL NEWS DID PADMÉ HAVE FOR ANAKIN WHEN HE RETURNED TO CORUSCANT?

4 WHAT HAPPENED IN ANAKIN'S NIGHTMARES?

48

5 WHO TOOK CONTROL OF THE JEDI COUNCIL?

6 WHICH SITH LORD DID PALPATINE TELL ANAKIN ABOUT IN THE GALAXIES OPERA HOUSE?

7 WHERE DID GENERAL GRIEVOUS GO INTO HIDING FROM THE JEDI?

8 WHAT WAS ORDER 66?

9 HOW MANY JEDI DID PALPATINE KILL ALTOGETHER WHEN MACE WINDU CAME TO ARREST HIM?

10 WHAT DID PALPATINE TELL ANAKIN HAD HAPPENED TO PADMÉ?

SCORE:

SUDOKU CHALLENGE

This puzzle will test your mental powers to the limit. Set a timer to record how long it takes and write your score in the box at the bottom of the page.

Remember, each row and column must include numbers 1 to 9 in any order. Also, each small 3 by 3 square must include numbers 1 to 9.

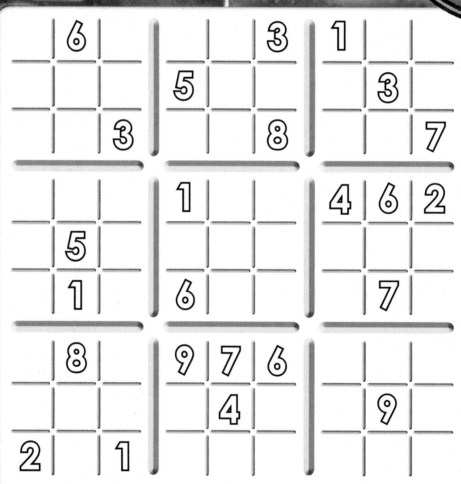

WHAT WAS YOUR SCORE?

SPOT THE DIFFERENCE

LUKE AND HAN SOLO SAVED PRINCESS LEIA FROM THE CLUTCHES OF DARTH VADER. THESE TWO PICTURES OF THAT DARING RESCUE LOOK THE SAME, BUT THERE ARE TEN SUBTLE DIFFERENCES. CAN YOU SPOT THEM ALL?

THE REVENGE OF THE SITH

1 General Grievous has kidnapped Chancellor Palpatine. Obi-Wan and Anakin go to the rescue.

2 The Jedi infiltrate Grievous's ship and find the Chancellor tied to a chair.

3 Count Dooku appears and the three Jedi duel.

4 Count Dooku knocks Obi-Wan out, but Anakin slices off Count Dooku's head.

5 The Jedi fight General Grievous for their lives.

6 The cruiser is about to crash and Grievous escapes.

7 Anakin uses the Force to steady the ship and land on Coruscant.

8 Back on Coruscant, Padmé tells Anakin that she is pregnant.

9 Darth Sidious tells General Grievous that the death of Count Dooku was planned.

10 Anakin dreams that Padmé will die in childbirth.

11 Yoda warns Anakin that the fear of loss is a path to the dark side.

12 Palpatine appoints Anakin as his representative on the Jedi Council.

THE REVENGE OF THE SITH

14 The Jedi refuse to give Anakin the title of 'Master'.

13 Some senators believe that the Chancellor is an enemy of democracy.

16 Obi-Wan finds and destroys General Grievous.

15 Palpatine tells Anakin that the Sith found a way to conquer death.

18 Palpatine and Mace duel, and Anakin watches in horror.

17 The Chancellor admits that he is a Sith Lord, and Anakin reports him to Mace Windu.

19 Mace prepares to kill Palpatine, but Anakin cuts off his lightsaber hand.

20 Palpatine flings Mace Windu to his death and cackles with pleasure.

21 Palpatine turns Anakin turns to the ways of the Sith and names him Darth Vader.

22 Anakin destroys the younglings while Palpatine issues Order 66: kill all Jedi.

23 Across the galaxy, Jedi are struck down by their own clone troops.

24 Palpatine sends Anakin to Mustafar to kill the Separatist leaders.

THE REVENGE OF THE SITH

25 Obi-Wan and Yoda are broken-hearted. They must kill Palpatine and Anakin.

26 Anakin kills the Separatist leaders, consumed with bloodshed and hatred.

27 Palpatine decrees that the Republic will become the first Galactic Empire.

28 When Padmé follows Anakin, Obi-Wan hides on her ship.

30 Obi-Wan and Anakin begin a deadly duel beside the boiling lava of Mustafar.

29 Padmé follows Anakin, but he thinks she has betrayed him and chokes her.

31 Darth Sidious and Yoda duel, but the Sith Master is triumphant.

32 Obi-Wan defeats Anakin and leaves him to burn in the lava.

33 Droid medics try to save Padmé, but she has lost the will to live.

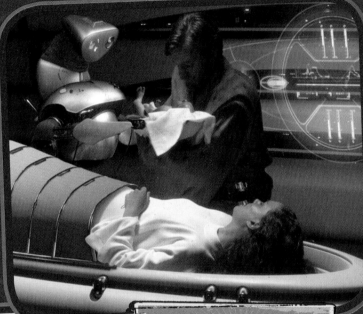

34 Padmé gives birth to a boy and a girl, and then dies.

35 Palpatine saves Darth Vader's life and tells him that he killed Padmé.

36 The Skywalker twins are hidden in the hope that one day they will save the galaxy.

ANAGRAM ATTACK

Whose names are hidden in these tricky anagrams?

1 PALE PAINT

2 A TOY DREAMS

3 DUO COOK NUT

4 WARLIKE YANK SANK

5 HALT A DRUM

6 MAMA AIDED PAL

7 BAUBLES

8 OAT FAN JET

Name the Historical Event

LOOK CLOSELY AT THESE PICTURES. ONE EVENT IN HISTORY LINKS THEM ALL TOGETHER. CAN YOU WORK OUT WHAT IT IS?

YOUR ANSWER

THE SEPARATISTS

Under the guidance of Count Dooku, the Separatists wanted to destroy the Republic and replace it with a system that would help them make more money. They didn't care about anything except lining their own pockets. As the Confederacy of Independent Systems, they comprised many different groups and guilds.

TRADE FEDERATION

The Trade Federation was a group of merchants and transportation providers that controlled shipping throughout the galaxy.

Its leaders allied themselves with Darth Sidious, who encouraged them to invade Naboo. Even though this venture failed, the Trade Federation became committed to the Separatist cause, and added its droid army to the growing Separatist forces.

THE CORPORATE ALLIANCE

The Corporate Alliance acted as a negotiating body for many of the galaxy's most influential commercial firms. The Corporate Alliance sided with the Separatists and was promised limitless profit.

THE COMMERCE GUILD

The Commerce Guild controlled many commodities and interests. At its heart were businesses involved in the acquisition, refinement and production of raw materials. The Guild's president, Shu Mai, could not resist the lure of money, and she committed the forces of the Commerce Guild to the Separatist movement.

POGGLE THE LESSER

Poggle the Lesser was the Archduke of Geonosis, but he had been born into a low caste. Through greed and determination, he overturned the strict traditions of the Geonosians and became their leader, murdering anyone who stood in his way.

Poggle was ruthless and hungry for power. His command staff was made from a bone of an enemy whom he murdered, although that may have been a myth. He met his death at the hands of Darth Vader.

NUTE GUNRAY

Nute Gunray was the Viceroy of the Trade Federation. Even as a Neimoidian, he was remarkable for his cut-throat business ethics. If something put money in his pocket, he couldn't care less about the effect on people or the environment. He left many planets dead and barren.

Despite leading the blockade against Naboo, he was able to buy his way out of trouble and retain his position. The temptation of Count Dooku's offer to join the Separatists was too great to withstand.

THE DEATH OF THE SEPARATISTS

When he issued Order 66 to kill all Jedi, Darth Sidious no longer needed the Separatist leaders. They had just been puppets in his plan to rule the galaxy. Darth Vader was sent to destroy them, and his lightsaber sliced through them all.

PERSONAL PREDICTOR

What will 2011 hold for you, your home planet and the galaxy? Use this space to make some predictions, and then check back throughout the year to see if you were right.

HOPES FOR FRIENDS

WHAT WILL YOU BE DOING ON THIS DAY A YEAR FROM NOW?

NEW YEAR'S RESOLUTIONS

WHAT WILL IMPROVE IN 2011?

TOP TEN PREDICTIONS

WHAT WILL WORSEN IN 2011?

TIME LINE

The Old Republic

-5,000,0000,000 Galaxy forms
-35,000 Birth of the Rakata Empire
-27,500 Alderaan colonized
-25,200 Fall of the Rakata Empire
-25,100 Treaty of Vontor
-25,100 Corellians and Duros
    introduced to hyperspace
-25,000 Perlemian Trade Route
    Corellian Run established
    Duros colonize Neimoidia
    1st Galactic Republic formed
    Creation of the Jedi Order
-17,000 First Alsakan crisis
-8000 Republic outpost on Malastare
-7000 Hundred-Year Darkness
-5500 Rimma Trade Route origin
-5000 Unification Wars End
-5000 Great Hyperspace War
-5000 Fall of the Sith Empire
-4250 Vultar Cataclysm
<-4000 Gank Massacre
-4015 Great Droid Revolution
-4000 Battle of Basilisk
-4000 Beast Wars of Onderon
-3998 Freedon Nadd Uprising
-3996 The Great Sith War
-3995 Mandalorian Wars begin
-3986 Ulic Qel-Droma's redemption
-3964 The Hunt for Zayne Carrick
-3961 Jedi Civil War
-3956 Malak War (Return of Revan)
-3951 Return of the Exile
-3900 Naboo colonized
-3653 Treaty of Coruscant
-3000 Hydian Way route blazed
-2000 New Sith Wars begin
-1003 Rise of Darth Bane
-1000 Battle of Ruusan
-1000 Sith go into hiding

Rise of the Empire

-896 Yoda born
-600 Jabba the Hutt born
-490 Corporate Sector formed
-350 Trade Federation established
-340 Chu'unthor crashes on Dathomir
-200 Chewbacca born
-102 Count Dooku born
-92 Qui-Gon born
-57 Obi-Wan born
-50 Arkanian Revolution
-46 Amidala born
-46 Veruna becomes King
-44 Obi-Wan becomes a Padawan
-44 Stark Hyperspace War

-41.9 Anakin born
-37 Mission to Ord Mantell
-32.5 Eriadu trade summit
-32.5 Amidala elected Queen
-32.5 Maul infiltrates Black Sun
-32 THE PHANTOM MENACE
-32 Battle of Naboo
-32 Palpatine elected Chancellor
-32 Count Dooku leaves the Jedi Order
-32 Jango Fett chose to be clone host
-31 Death of Sharad Hett
-29 Mission to Zonama Sekot
-29 Han Solo born
-28 Anakin builds his lightsaber
-27 Outbound Flight
-22.1 Ansion threatens to secede
-22 ATTACK OF THE CLONES
-22 Battle of Geonosis
-22 Clone Wars begin
-22 Marriage of Anakin and Padmé
-21 Anakin becomes a Jedi Knight
-21 Battle of Christophsis
-21 Battle of Teth [ACWT]
-21 Hunt for the Malevolence [ACW1]
-21 Battle of Ryloth [ACW1]
-21 Second Battle of Geonosis [ACW2]
-19 REVENGE OF THE SITH
-19 Battle of Coruscant
-19 Death of Mace Windu
-19 Anakin becomes Darth Vader
-19 Order Sixty-Six
-19 Palpatine declares himself Emperor
-19 Vader/Obi-Wan duel on Mustafar
-19 Luke & Leia born
-19 Death of Padmé Amidala
-18 Eye of Palpatine
-7 Disaster on Falleen
-4 Lando Calrissian's adventures
-2 Chewie marries Malla
-2 Corellian Treaty
-1 Search for the Yavin Vassilika

The Rebellion

0 Alliance steals Death Star plans
0 STAR WARS – A NEW HOPE
0 Princess Leia captured
0 Luke meets R2-D2 and C-3PO
0 Obi-Wan shows Luke the Force
0 Emperor dissolves Senate
0 Luke meets Han Solo
0 Destruction of Alderaan
0 Obi-Wan becomes one with the Force
0 Heroes escape Death Star
0 Battle of Yavin
0 Death of Tarkin
0 Destruction of the Death Star
0 Walex Blissex joins the Alliance
0 A-wing designed
0.5 Luke Skywalker discovers Hoth
0.5 Alliance flees Yavin
0.5 Dodonna captured
1 B-wing designed
1 Crix Madine defects to Alliance
2 Circarpous joins Alliance
2 Alliance builds base on Hoth
2 B-wing brought to the Alliance
3 THE EMPIRE STRIKES BACK
3 Battle of Hoth
3 Luke trains on Dagobah
3 Han Solo frozen in carbonite
3 Luke duels Vader on Cloud City
3.5 Black Sun plot to kill Luke
3.5 Boba Fett delivers Solo to Jabba
3.5 Death of Prince Xizor
4 RETURN OF THE JEDI
4 Boba Fett falls into the Sarlacc
4 Death of Jabba the Hutt
4 Death of Yoda
4 Battle of Endor
4 Death of the Emperor
4 Redemption/death of Anakin
Skywalker
4 Destruction of Death Star II

LOST LINKS

Can you re-link these famous quotes with the scene they came from?

A. "Fought well you have, my old Padawan."

B. "Your powers are weak, old man."

C. "You don't know the power of the Dark Side, I must obey my master."

D. "Are you an angel?"

E. "Luminous beings are we, not this crude matter."

F. "Lost a planet, Master Obi-Wan has. How embarrassing."

G. "Twilight is upon me, and soon, night must fall."

H. "You are on the council, but we do not grant you the rank of master."

I. "I don't want to hear any more about Obi-Wan. The Jedi turned against me."

J. "The ability to speak does not make you intelligent."

K. "I have the death sentence on twelve systems."

L. "I am altering the deal. Pray I don't alter it any further."

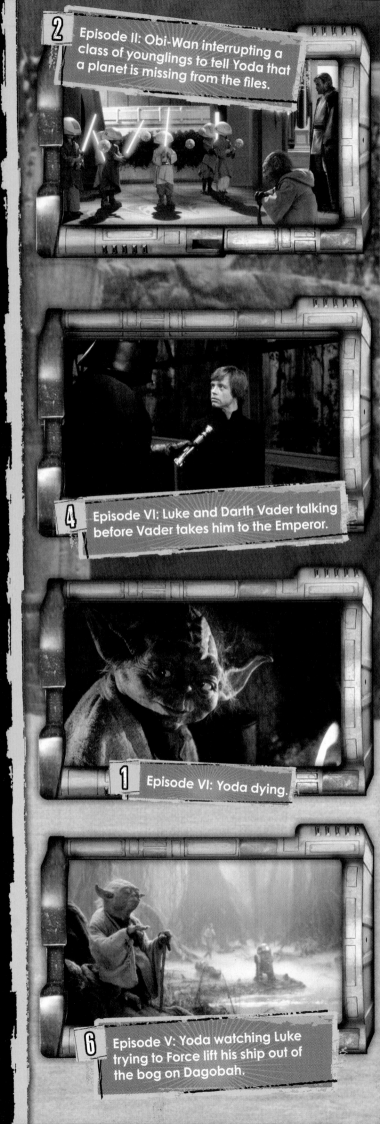

2 Episode II: Obi-Wan interrupting a class of younglings to tell Yoda that a planet is missing from the files.

4 Episode VI: Luke and Darth Vader talking before Vader takes him to the Emperor.

1 Episode VI: Yoda dying.

6 Episode V: Yoda watching Luke trying to Force lift his ship out of the bog on Dagobah.

11 Episode III: Anakin talking to Padmé on Mustafar just before he Force chokes her.

9 Episode I: The first time Anakin and Padmé meet – in Watto's shop.

3 Episode IV: Obi-Wan and Darth Vader about to have their final duel.

12 Episode IV: Luke talking to Dr Evazan in the Mos Eisley cantina.

7 Episode V: Darth Vader talking to Lando after he has captured Leia and Han.

10 Episode I: The first time Qui-Gon meets Jar Jar Binks.

8 Episode III: Anakin joining the council on Palpatine's orders, and Mace Windu addressing him.

5 Episode II: Yoda and Dooku having a lightsaber duel.

GREETINGS!

Use these templates to create your own greetings cards, complete with images of your favourite Star Wars characters.

You will need:
- A5 white card • Tracing paper
- Pencil • Colouring pens or paints

1 Fold the A5 card in half to make a card.
2 Carefully trace your favourite picture onto the front of the card.
3 Colour in your picture.
4 Choose a Star Wars greeting to write inside your card.
5 Give your card in person, or recycle an envelope and decorate it with Star Wars images.

FEEL THE FORCE!

MAY THE FORCE BE WITH YOU!

THE FORCE IS STRONG WITH YOU!

WHEN 900 YEARS OLD YOU REACH, LOOK AS GOOD YOU WILL NOT!

GALACTIC QUIZ PART 4

ANSWER THESE QUESTIONS AS QUICKLY AS YOU CAN, AND DON'T FORGET TO KEEP SCORE!

1 ON WHICH PLANET WAS LUKE LIVING WHEN HE FIRST MET R2-D2 AND C-3PO?

2 WHICH TRADERS SOLD LUKE THE DROIDS?

3 WHAT ANIMALS DO THE SAND PEOPLE USE FOR TRANSPORT?

4 WHAT IS PRINCESS LEIA'S HOME PLANET?

5 WHAT WAS THE SMALL TARGET FOR THE ALLIANCE ATTACK ON THE DEATH STAR?

6 HOW BIG WAS THE TARGET FOR THE ALLIANCE ATTACK ON THE DEATH STAR?

7 AS THE FIGHTERS BEGAN THEIR ATTACK SEQUENCES ON THE DEATH STAR, THE PILOTS SWITCHED ALL POWER TO _____.

8 WHOSE VOICE DID LUKE HEAR WHEN HE WAS STARTING HIS ATTACK RUN?

9 HOW LONG DID IT TAKE FOR THE *MILLENNIUM FALCON* TO DO THE KESSEL RUN?

10 WHO WAS ANAKIN SKYWALKER'S STEP-SISTER-IN-LAW?

SCORE:

A NEW HOPE

1 Princess Leia is carrying important plans to the Rebels, but Darth Vader is chasing her.

2 Princess Leia passes the plans to R2-D2 and tells him to find Obi-Wan Kenobi.

3 R2-D2 and C-3P0 escape to Tatooine. They are captured and sold to Owen Lars.

4 Owen tells his nephew, Luke Skywalker, to clean the droids up.

5 Luke has spent his life on Tatooine, but his heart yearns for adventure.

6 Luke discovers part of a message from Princess Leia.

7 R2-D2 pretends to know nothing about the message or the Princess.

8 Luke mentions the message to his aunt and uncle, who seem worried.

10 Next morning, Luke and C-3PO follow the disobedient droid.

9 R2-D2 sets off to find Obi-Wan Kenobi.

12 In the message, the Princess begs Obi-Wan to take the plans to her father on Alderaan.

11 Luke finds Obi-Wan Kenobi and learns that his father was a Jedi Knight.

A NEW HOPE

13 Darth Vader's storm troopers kill Luke's aunt and uncle and destroy their home.

14 Luke agrees to join Obi-Wan on his mission to Alderaan.

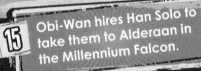
15 Obi-Wan hires Han Solo to take them to Alderaan in the Millennium Falcon.

16 Han owes money to the gangster Jabba the Hutt.

17 Grand Moff Tarkin will destroy Alderaan unless Leia reveals the location of the Rebel base.

18 Princess Leia gives a false location, but Tarkin destroys Alderaan and condemns her to death.

19 The Millennium Falcon arrives and the Death Star captures them with a tractor beam.

20 Darth Vader senses Obi-Wan's presence and is determined to destroy his old Master.

21 Obi-Wan goes to deactivate the tractor beam.

22 Luke, Han and Chewbacca set off to find the Princess.

23 They rescue the Princess and battle past Imperial troops to reach their ship.

24 Obi-Wan deactivates the tractor beam and then meets Darth Vader.

A NEW HOPE

25 Obi-Wan accepts death without fear.

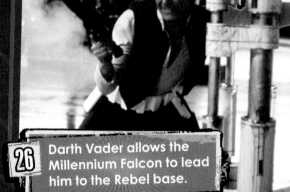

26 Darth Vader allows the Millennium Falcon to lead him to the Rebel base.

27 A precise hit on the Death Star's thermal exhaust port will destroy the battle station.

28 Luke will pilot a fighter, but Han leaves to pay his debt to Jabba the Hutt.

29 The Rebel pilots take off and head towards their evil enemy.

30 Darth Vader pilots his own vessel and destroys many Rebel fighters.

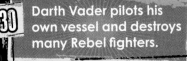

31 The Rebel leaders keep missing the tiny target.

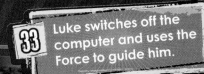

32 Darth Vader is close on Luke's tail!

33 Luke switches off the computer and uses the Force to guide him.

34 Darth Vader is behind Luke when the Millennium Falcon blasts his fighter. Han is back!

35 Luke fires and the Death Star explodes into millions of tiny pieces.

36 The Rebels cheer as Luke, Chewbacca and Han receive medals from Princess Leia.

Tatooine

Tatooine was an out-of-the-way planet, and yet it featured at the heart of some of the most important events in the galaxy. Anakin Skywalker, the Chosen One, was discovered by Jedi Master Qui-Gon Jinn on Tatooine. It was here that Luke Skywalker grew up and learned of his true destiny, and it was here that he met Han Solo.

Anakin Skywalker

Anakin grew up on Tatooine as a slave boy, owned by a Toydarian junk dealer. He was strongly attuned to the Force, and was intrigued by stories of the Jedi Order. Anakin was competitive and daring, but also loving and kind.

Anakin was a gifted pilot and the only human capable of handling the extreme speeds of Podracing. His connection with the Force was the reason for his lightning-fast reactions.

Shmi Skywalker

When she was a child, Shmi Skywalker was abducted by pirates who sold her into slavery. She worked hard to give Anakin a good and happy life, but she also sensed that his special abilities would lead him to a better future than she could offer.

After Qui-Gon Jinn took her son away to join the Jedi Order, Shmi was sold to a moisture farmer called Cliegg Lars, who freed her and married her. She lived on his moisture farm, and loved his son Owen as if he were her own.

Watto

Watto was a Toydarian junk dealer who lived on Tatooine. His shop was a magical treasure trove of old machinery and spare parts. Watto owned Shmi and Anakin as slaves. He was greedy and immoral, and he lost Anakin while betting on the Boonta Eve Podrace with Qui-Gon Jinn.

Jawas

The Jawas lived in Tatooine's deserts, and they were a great threat to any droid that crossed their path. They scavenged for discarded scrap metal and lost droids. After they had refurbished their finds, they would sell them to moisture farmers. Jawas would cheat their customers if they could, but the moisture farmers had nowhere else to buy their droids.

Jawas' faces were permanently obscured by clouds of insects that were attracted by the terrible stench they gave off.

Sebulba

Sebulba was a cheating Podracing champion who cared more about winning than taking part. He had a massive ego and despised Anakin Skywalker because of his talent.

Jabba the Hutt

Jabba was a Hutt gangster who lived in a slovenly palace on Tatooine. He had made his fortune through piracy, slavery, gambling and the sale of stolen goods.

The decadence of his palace attracted the scum of the galaxy, and Jabba's constant companions were thieves, smugglers, assassins and spies.

Jabba's legless, tapered body was coated in slime. His snake-like eyes glinted with the love of power and depravity. His idea of entertainment was torturing and humiliating his subjects.

When Jabba hired Han Solo to smuggle glitterstim spice, he started a chain of events that would end in his own destruction.

Tusken Raiders

Tusken Raiders were savage nomads who roamed the rocky Jundland Wastes of Tatooine. They were also known as Sand People, and would attack with almost no reason. Male Tusken Raiders were the most aggressive, but all of them were dangerous.

The Sand People tamed a species called the bantha, and developed an almost telepathic link with them. A tribe member who had lost his bantha was seen as incomplete.

Podracing

Podracing was a high-speed sport that could trace its origins to ancient contests of animal-drawn chariots. Long ago, a foolhardy mechanic named Phoebos revisited the chariot design, replacing the cart with a repulsorlift Pod and the beasts of burden with rocket jet engines. A new and dangerous spectacle was created. In the waning years of the Republic, when prohibitive laws failed to extend to the Outer Rim Territories, Podracing was still quite successful despite being banned in the central systems.

The Cantina

Strange and dangerous aliens were the usual customers of the Cantina. An all-alien band called the Modal Nodes played in the corner, and there were only two rules; droids were not allowed inside, and if anyone got involved in a fight, they had to leave blasters out of it.

Mos Eisley

Mos Eisley was a pirate city and one of the largest spaceports on Tatooine. Although it was not the capital city, it had high status thanks to the trade and tourism industries. Jabba the Hutt had a house in the downtown area, and the city was always full of criminals who were passing through. They were usually to be found in the Cantina.

Modal Nodes

The cantina band was made up of Bith aliens playing various wind and percussion instruments. They were Jabba the Hutt's house band for a while, but when he grew tired of them they fled from Tatooine.

THE EMPIRE

When the Galactic Republic crumbled, many people hoped that the new Galactic Empire would be a better and less corrupt system of government. Too late, they realised that it was a tyrannical regime of terror. Personal liberties were crushed, and corrupt regional governors had absolute control over everyday affairs. The military maintained order through fear and cruelty. The galaxy was helpless in the hands of the wicked Emperor.

GRAND MOFF TARKIN

Grand Moff Tarkin was the mastermind of the Death Star project, and Imperial governor of the Outland Regions. He was extremely clever, but absolutely ruthless. He once landed his ship on top of hundreds of people who were protesting against taxation, crushing them to death.

ADMIRAL CONAN ANTONIO MOTTI

Admiral Motti was the senior Imperial commander in charge of operations aboard the first Death Star. In his arrogance, he refused to believe that anything could harm the battle station.

As someone who believed only in science and technology, he laughed at Darth Vader's devotion to the Force. In response, Darth Vader Force choked Motti. He did not kill him, but Motti learned a valuable lesson that day.

THE REBEL ALLIANCE

The Emperor taught his officers that the best way to keep order was by using fear. Power-crazed officers developed cruel methods to make people too scared to speak out against them. Despite this tyranny, a few resistance groups banded together to form the Alliance to Restore the Republic.

ADMIRAL OZZEL

The ignorant Admiral Ozzel was the Imperial Navy officer in command of the Imperial Death Squadron just before the Battle of Hoth. He had little talent for his job and no imagination. When Captain Piett reported signs of life in the Hoth system, Admiral Ozzel ignored him.

He then brought the Imperial fleet out of hyperspace too close to the system, alerting the Rebels to their presence. To punish him for his stupidity, Darth Vader strangled him and replaced him with Captain Piett.

THE DEATH STAR

The Death Star was the weapon to end all weapons – the symbol of ultimate destruction. When fully charged, its superlaser was powerful enough to destroy a planet.

The Emperor was enraged when the Rebel Alliance destroyed the Death Star at the Battle of Yavin. He began work on a second superweapon – a Death Star that would be even more powerful than the first, and totally indestructible.

THE DEATH OF THE EMPIRE

The Battle of Endor was plotted by Emperor Palpatine. He intended to trap and destroy the Rebels once and for all. However, he underestimated the resourcefulness of the Rebels and his power over Darth Vader.

He paid for his mistake with his life, and the Imperial reign of terror ended. As the Rebels began forming a New Republic, the galaxy celebrated the return to freedom.

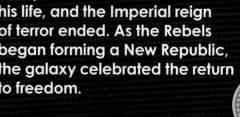

THE EMPIRE STRIKES BACK

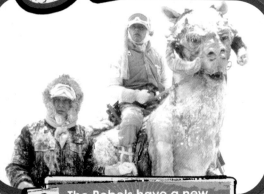

1 The Rebels have a new secret base on the remote ice world of Hoth.

2 Darth Vader has deployed thousands of probes to find Luke. Luke spots one of the probes.

3 A vicious snow beast attacks him and drags him away to its icy lair.

4 Han wants to leave to pay Jabba the Hutt. Leia is furious with him.

5 When he hears that Luke is missing, Han goes out to search for his friend.

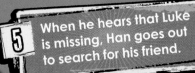

6 Meanwhile, Luke uses his lightsaber to set himself free and escape.

7 Luke collapses in the freezing snow and sees a vision of Obi-Wan Kenobi.

8 Obi-Wan tells Luke to go to the Dagobah system and learn from Yoda.

9 Han finds Luke and saves his life by cutting open a Tauntaun to keep them warm.

10 Darth Vader sets a course for Hoth. Sensors at the base warn the Rebels.

11 Darth Vader arrives before the Rebels have evacuated, and a ground-shaking battle begins.

12 Rebel forces are evacuated while Luke risks his life to destroy the Imperial walkers.

13 Luke flies away with R2-D2, setting a course for the Dagobah system.

14 Darth Vader orders a motley crew of bounty hunters to capture the Millennium Falcon.

15 The Emperor hopes to turn the son of Skywalker to the dark side.

16 Han and his friends escape, but Boba Fett is on their trail.

17 Han heads for a nearby mining colony, which is run by his friend Lando Calrissian.

18 Luke crashes into a swamp on Dagobah.

19 Luke meets a small, wrinkled creature with green skin, and is irritable and rude – until he realises this is Yoda.

20 Yoda agrees to train Luke, but it is a long and difficult process.

21 Darth Vader has offered Lando a simple choice – lose his friends or kill his people.

22 Lando delivers his friends into Darth Vader's hands, hating himself for doing it.

23 Luke has a vision of Han and Leia in danger. He has to go and help them!

24 Yoda and Obi-Wan warn him not to leave without completing his training.

THE EMPIRE STRIKES BACK

25 Luke promises to return and complete his training, but he must save his friends.

26 Darth Vader freezes Han in carbonite and lets Boba Fett take him to Jabba the Hutt.

27 Luke arrives at the mining colony and walks straight into a trap.

28 Luke faces the evil Darth Vader. They ignite their lightsabers and duel.

29 Guilty Lando frees Leia, C-3PO and Chewbacca and they escape in the Millennium Falcon.

30 Luke defends himself against Darth Vader, using the skills that Yoda has taught him.

31 Darth Vader's lightsaber swipes off Luke's right hand.

32 Darth Vader reveals that he is Luke's father and tries to turn him to the dark side.

33 Luke would rather die than turn to the dark side. He rolls off the edge of the platform.

34 Luke's fall is broken by a metal structure below the city. He clings on desperately.

35 Luke calls for Leia in his mind, and she orders the others to turn the ship around.

36 As Luke is rescued, Darth Vader senses that he is still alive.

GALACTIC QUIZ PART 5

ANSWER THESE QUESTIONS AND RECORD YOUR SCORE BEFORE MOVING ON TO THE FINAL PART OF THE QUIZ.

1 WHAT DID LANDO CALRISSIAN ONCE OWN THAT LATER BELONGED TO HAN SOLO?

2 WHERE DID DARTH VADER'S PROBE DISCOVER LUKE HIDING?

3 WHAT WAS THE NAME OF THE SNOW BEAST THAT ATTACKED LUKE?

4 ABOVE WHAT PLANET DID CLOUD CITY FLOAT?

88

5 WHAT DID DARTH VADER USE TO FREEZE HAN SOLO?

6 WHICH BOUNTY HUNTER TRACKED HAN SOLO AND TOLD DARTH VADER WHERE TO FIND HIM?

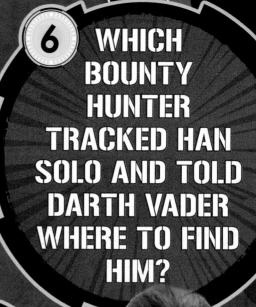

7 WHY DID LUKE LEAVE DAGOBAH?

8 HOW DID LUKE GET LEIA TO TURN BACK TO RESCUE HIM?

9 WHICH DROID GOT A RIDE ON CHEWBACCA'S BACK?

10 WHAT DID HAN SAY WHEN LEIA TOLD HIM SHE LOVED HIM?

SCORE:

MISSING WORDS

THERE ARE SOME WORDS MISSING FROM THESE PHRASES. THE MISSING WORDS HAVE BEEN COLLECTED AT THE BOTTOM OF THE PAGE. CAN YOU RECOGNISE AND COMPLETE ALL THE PHRASES?

1. [   ] matters not.
2. I have [   ] you, Anakin.
3. Only a [   ] deals in absolutes.
4. Try not. [   ], or [   ]. There is no [   ].
5. I have a [   ] about this.
6. There's always a bigger [   ].
7. The fear of [   ] is a path to the [   ].
8. Truly wonderful the mind of a [   ] is.
9. It's against my [   ] to impersonate a [   ].
10. From my point of view the [   ] are evil.
11. Obi-Wan never told you what happened to your [   ]
12. Your [   ] can deceive you; don't [   ] them.

		DARK SIDE	DEITY	DO
BAD FEELING	CHILD			
		FATHER	FISH	JEDI	LOSS
DO NOT	EYES	FAILED			
	PROGRAMMING	SITH LORD	SIZE	TRUST	TRY

90

TRUE OR FALSE?

Put your memory to the test. Read each statement and decide if it is true or false.

1 Anakin Skywalker built R2-D2.
☐ TRUE ☑ FALSE

2 Kamino is a type of acid.
☐ TRUE ☑ FALSE

3 Luke's uncle did not want him to follow in his father's footsteps.
☐ TRUE ☑ FALSE

4 Master Yoda was born on Dagobah.
☑ TRUE ☐ FALSE

5 Luke Skywalker grew up on Dantooine.
☐ TRUE ☑ FALSE

6 Padmé Naberrie was once Queen of Naboo.
☑ TRUE ☐ FALSE

7 The Jedi who killed Jango Fett had red hair.
☐ TRUE ☑ FALSE

8 Princess Leia is Anakin Skywalker's niece.
☐ TRUE ☑ FALSE

9 Mace Windu cut Anakin's hand off.
☐ TRUE ☑ FALSE

10 Anakin Skywalker was the last person his mother saw before she died.
☐ TRUE ☐ FALSE

11 Chewbacca rescued Han Solo from slavery.
☑ TRUE ☐ FALSE

12 General Grievous designed the Death Star.
☐ TRUE ☑ FALSE

13 Fear is the path to the Dark Side.
☑ TRUE ☐ FALSE

14 The Sith know the secret to everlasting life.
☑ TRUE ☐ FALSE

15 Senator Amidala married in secret.
☐ TRUE ☑ FALSE

DARK GLOBE

Instead of the traditional snow globe, why not make a Sith globe instead? Follow these instructions to create this dark Christmas decoration.

Always get an **adult to help you** when using strong glue or baking in the oven.

YOU WILL NEED:

 Small glass jar with screw-on lid

 Miniature model of Darth Vader or black modelling clay

Glycerine

 Black glitter

 Strong glue

1 If you are using clay, make a small model of Darth Vader. Use the picture to help you.

2 Bake according to the clay instructions.

3 Glue your clay model or miniature onto the inside of the jar lid.

4 Fill the jar with water and add a tablespoon of glycerine.

5 Sprinkle some glitter into the jar.

6 Brush some strong glue around the rim of the jar.

7 Screw on the jar lid.

8 Wait until the glue has dried, then turn your globe upside down and watch the darkness surround the Sith Lord!

SITH LORD

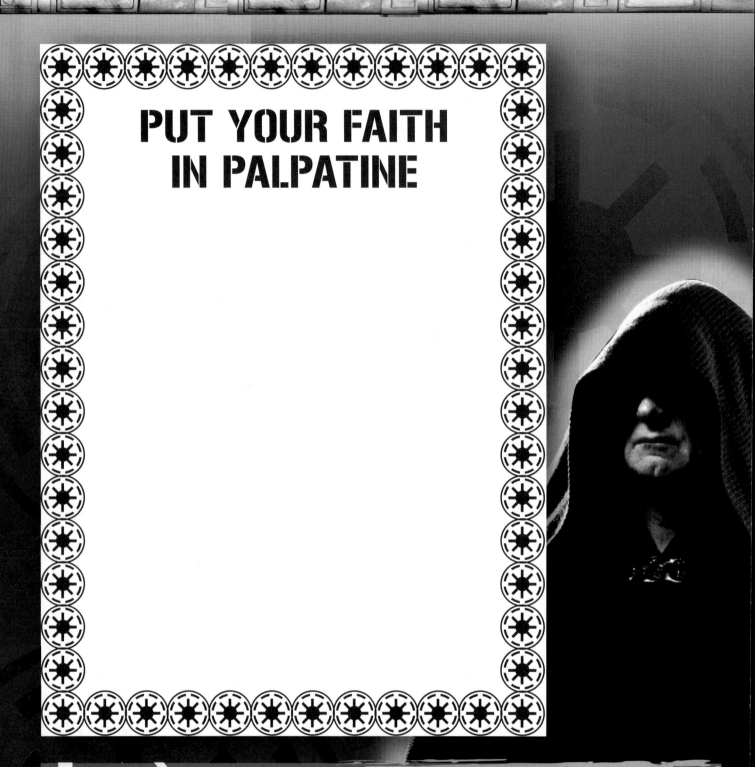

PUT YOUR FAITH IN PALPATINE

Palpatine has ordered a series of posters to be placed around Coruscant, reminding people of his wisdom, kindness and honesty.

Can you design an eye-catching poster to fit with the words he has chosen?

HOME PLANETS

Look carefully at these pictures.
Can you match the characters who come from the same planet?
Draw lines to connect them.

How many planets are represented here?

There are................planets represented here.

DESIGN YOUR OWN
STORM TROOPER

The Rise of the Storm Troopers

The Emperor's Storm Troopers began as Clone Troopers in the battle against the Separatists. Examine their development into the terrifying battalions of the Empire.

Then use the space provided to draw a new generation of Storm Trooper. How will they develop next? What tools and weapons will they carry? Complete your design by labelling it and colouring it in.

Storm Trooper

- Suit made from 18 pieces of hardened plastoid composite armour
- Helmet with polarised lenses, transmitters and sensor arrays
- Utility belt containing emergency batteries, ammunition, a grappling hook and a thermal detonator
- Blaster pistol
- Blaster rifle

Clone Trooper

- Thigh plate • Spare blaster igniters • Utility belt
- High-traction soles • Helmet with built-in comlink
- Knee plate • Breath filter

THE RETURN OF THE JEDI

1 Han Solo has been hanging on Jabba's wall as a carbonite image for far too long.

2 Luke, Leia, Lando and the droids face the disgusting Hutt lord.

3 Jabba underestimates Luke's Jedi abilities and pays with his life.

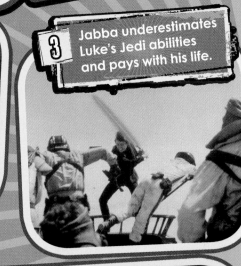

4 Leia and Han go to join the Rebels, while Luke returns to the Dagobah system.

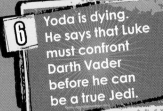

5 A new Death Star is being built, and the Emperor is plotting Luke's downfall.

6 Yoda is dying. He says that Luke must confront Darth Vader before he can be a true Jedi.

7 As Luke grieves, a vision of Obi-Wan tells him how his father turned to the dark side.

8 Luke refuses to kill his own father. Obi-Wan tells Luke that Leia is his twin.

9 The Rebels plan to attack the Death Star. They must deactivate its energy shield, which is powered from Endor.

10 Han will lead the strike team to Endor. Lando will lead the attack on the Death Star.

11 When Han's strike team lands on Endor, Darth Vader senses that Luke is there.

12 On the forest-covered moon, the strike team befriends a tribe of Ewoks.